Guess Who?

Can you guess who is getting ready?

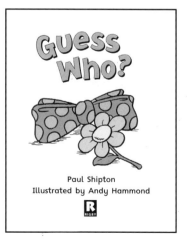

Paul Shipton
Illustrated by Andy Hammond

G000152120

Walkthrough

This is the back cover.

This is the blurb.

Let's read the blurb together.

'Can you guess who is getting ready?'

Does the picture give you a clue?

(Prompt for suggestions.)

Walkthrough

This is the title page.
Let's read the title again together.
'Guess Who?'

Are there any more clues on this page to help you guess who he is?

Read the names of the author and illustrator to the children.

This is the publisher's logo.

Walkthrough

What is the boy putting on?

What might he say?

 Observe and Prompt

Word Recognition

- Check the children are reading the CVC word 'put' using their decoding skills. Can they sound and blend p-u-t through the word?

- If the children have difficulty with the word 'shirt', ask them if they recognise the initial letters and sound – 'sh'. Then tell them the word and model the reading of it for them.

I put on my shirt.

2

👁 Observe and Prompt

Language Comprehension

- Ask the children what the boy is doing.

- What do the children think the boy might put on next?

Walkthrough

What is the boy putting on here?

 Observe and Prompt

Word Recognition

- Check the children can read 'I', 'on' and 'my'. (These are sight words – words likely to be in their store of familiar words.)
- The word 'tie' will not be decodable for children at this stage. Tell them this word.

I put on my tie.

4

5

Language Comprehension

- Ask the children what the boy is putting on now.
- Ask the children where the boy is looking.

Walkthrough

What's he putting on here?

Can you guess who he is yet?

 Observe and Prompt

Word Recognition

- The word 'coat' may not be decodable for children at this stage. Tell them this word and model the reading of it for them.

I put on my coat.

6

6

 Observe and Prompt

Language Comprehension

- Ask the children what is happening now.
- Can the children guess who the boy might be?
- How do the children think the boy is feeling?

Walkthrough

What is he putting on now?

What do you think he will put on next?

 Observe and Prompt

Word Recognition

- If the children have difficulty with the word 'socks', ask them if they recognise the initial letter and sound – 's'. Then encourage them to use their decoding skills to read the word, assisting them with the letters 'ck' if necessary.

I put on my socks.

8

9

 Observe and Prompt

Language Comprehension

- Ask the children what the boy is putting on now.
- Do the children think he is nearly ready?

Walkthrough

What's he putting on now? Were you right?

Do you notice the difference?

 Observe and Prompt

Word Recognition

- The word 'shoes' may not be fully decodable for the children at this stage. Ask the children if they recognise the initial letters and sound – 'sh'. Then tell them the word and model the reading of it for them.

I put on my shoes.

10

11

Observe and Prompt

Language Comprehension

- Ask the children what the boy is putting on now.

- Do the children think these are normal shoes?

- Can the children guess who the boy is going to be?

11

Walkthrough

What is he putting on his head?

Have you any ideas about what he is going to be?

 Observe and Prompt

Word Recognition

- Check the children are reading 'wig' using their decoding skills. Can they sound out and blend w-i-g all through the word?
- Check the children can read the sight words 'I', 'on' and 'my'.

I put on my wig.

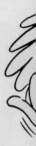

12

13

 Observe and Prompt

Language Comprehension

- Ask the children what is happening now.
- Do the children think the boy is ready?

Walkthrough

What is he putting on his head now?

Do you know who he is now?

What else does he need to put on?

 Observe and Prompt

Word Recognition

- Check the children are reading 'hat' using their decoding skills. Can they sound out and blend h-a-t all through the word?

I put on my hat.

14

15

 Observe and Prompt

Language Comprehension

- Ask the children what the boy is putting on now.

- How do they think the boy is feeling?

- Do the children think the boy needs to put on anything else?

15

Walkthrough

What's the last thing that he put on?

Are you right? He is a ...

I put on my nose!

16

 Observe and Prompt

Language Comprehension

- Check the children understand what has happened at the end of the story. What has the boy dressed up as?

- Check the children are reading with expression.

- Have any of the children ever seen a clown?

 Observe and Prompt

Word Recognition

- The word 'nose' may not be decodable for the children at this stage. Tell the children this word and model the reading of it for them.